100 Days of Drawing

Welcome to *100 Days of Drawing*!

Drawing every single day can be a challenge. Whether you're not feeling inspired, worrying that a piece isn't going to be good enough, or just can't think of anything to draw, we've all had creative block before.

100 Days of Drawing is a simple yet effective sketchbook that can help you overcome artist's block and get you in a state flow, strengthen your drawing skills and get you on the road to being an effective creative thinker.

So with this sketchbook be sure to take it out each day and be inspired by the 100 prompts available to you. Becoming a great artist is all about consistency, not quantity. Don't focus on making the best drawing you can each day, but ensure you draw everyday – even if only for five minutes.

When we expose ourselves to small chunks of a skillset, we getting better and better, adapting with the challenges or setbacks along the way. So get excited and watch your drawing journey unfold.

Good luck!

FIRST 30 DAYS

In your first 30 days try not to focus on perfection but rather creativity.

When you see a prompt or shape, try and think of the most out-of-the-box idea you can that relates to it.

You can take a dark twist on a seemingly light prompt, try your hand at abstract art with a lone squiggle or bring in an element of comedy - something that could make you chuckle as you draw it.

The first 30 days are all about fun. Grow the passion and love for drawing this next month and don't take any prompt too seriously.

This is your sketchbook, so enjoy the process!

DAY 1
'BEGINNING'

Day 2
Build a drawing from the squiggle below

DAY 3
'COUNTDOWN'

Day 4
'ELECTRIC'

DAY 5
BUILD A DRAWING FROM THE SQUIGGLE BELOW

Day 6
'PRIDE'

Day 7
'SUSPENSE'

DAY 8
'ROCKET'

DAY 9
BUILD A DRAWING FROM THE SQUIGGLE BELOW

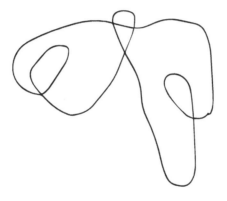

DAY 10
'VOICE'

DAY 11
'TATTOO'

Day 12
'GREEN'

DAY 13
BUILD A DRAWING FROM THE SQUIGGLE BELOW

DAY 14
'WANDER'

DAY 15
'RIVER'

DAY 16
'MIND'

DAY 17
'ENVY'

Day 19
'STORM'

DAY 20
'CRYSTAL'

DAY 21
'BRIDGE'

DAY 22
BUILD A DRAWING FROM THE SQUIGGLE BELOW

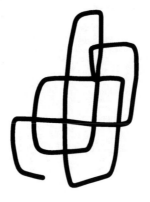

DAY 23
'MUD'

Day 24
'JEWEL'

DAY 25
'FRIEND'

DAY 26
BUILD A DRAWING FROM THE SQUIGGLE BELOW

DAY 27
'FRAGILE'

Day 28
'SHIP'

DAY 29
'SUMMIT'

Day 30
Draw how you feel looking back on your first 30 sketches

FIRST 30 DAYS DONE!

Congratulations! You've smashed through
your first 30 days! Let's use this time to reflect
about the journey so far...

My favourite drawing: _____

The most difficult prompt: _____

The most inspiring prompt:_____

I'm really good at: _____

I need to work on: _____

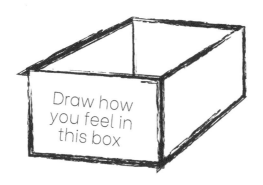

Draw how
you feel in
this box

ONWARDS TO 60!

Your next 30 days will focus on scenarios and world building.

When you see a prompt or shape, try and think of how you could build that one word or one line into a larger scene.

For example, if you see the prompt *running late*, try to fill the page with the scenario that embodies that prompt. Maybe that's a man running out the door of his messy apartment, or a teen chasing after a bus or even something completely out-of-the-box.

Make it yours and tell a story!

DAY 31
'A HOPELESS ROMANTIC WINDOW SHOPPING'

Day 32
'PSYCHIC READINGS ON SALE'

DAY 33
'BEFORE AND AFTER'

DAY 34
BUILD A WORLD FROM THE BELOW SKETCH

DAY 35
'CHRISTMAS IN SUMMERTIME'

DAY 36
'PORTRAIT OF A PIG'

DAY 37
BUILD A SCENE FROM THE BELOW SKETCH

DAY 38
'RETIRED DETECTIVE AT DINNER'

Day 39
'DOG WITH A BANDANA'

DAY 40
BUILD A SCENE FROM THE BELOW SKETCH

Day 41

'Doctor who loves to sew'

DAY 42
'RUNNING LATE'

DAY 43
'I'LL HAVE THE NUMBER 4, THANKS'

Day 44
Build a world from the below sketch

Day 45
'BIGGEST DAY OF THE YEAR'

DAY 46
'WE SCREAM FOR ICECREAM'

DAY 47
'BETTER THAN EVER'

Day 48
Build a world from the below sketch

DAY 49
'I WISH FOR...'

DAY 50
'MURDER ON THE DANCEFLOOR'

DAY 51
'TWO MEN DUEL'

Day 52
Build a scene from the below sketch

DAY 53
'STARGAZE ON THE ROOF'

DAY 54
'COWBOY GECKO'

DAY 56
'COZY WINTER'

DAY 57
BUILD A SCENE FROM THE BELOW SKETCH

DAY 58
'ACCOMPLISHED ANIMAL'

Day 59
'FRANTIC ZEN GARDEN'

DAY 60
BUILD A SCENE FROM THE BELOW SKETCH

FIRST 60 DAYS DONE!

Wow! 60 days already! It's time to reflect
about the journey so far...

My favourite drawing: _____

The most difficult prompt: _____

The most inspiring prompt: _____

I'm really good at: _____

I need to work on: _____

Add to this house, make it reflect
how you feel

Next stop, 75!

The next 15 days will focus on perspective.

Each prompt will give you an exercise to explore horizons, vanishing points and how you can change the entire mood of a sketch depending on perspective.

Once you master perspective your options will open up to a new world of possibilities. You can explore positions of your subject, art styles like surrealism and build more intricate worlds.

It's time to challenge yourself, let's draw!

DAY 61
CREATE A BEDROOM FROM THE PERSPECTIVE BELOW

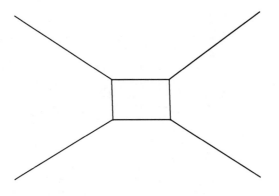

DAY 62
DRAW STEPS USING THESE VANISHING POINTS

*HINT

DAY 63
DRAW 8 CUBES FROM DIFFERENT
PERSPECTIVES BELOW

✕

*HINT

Day 64
Draw a prism below, then make it into interesting character

×

DAY 65
GIVE THE BELOW CHARACTER AN OUTFIT, IN LINE WITH THEIR DRAWN PERSPECTIVE

DAY 66
DRAW A CORNER OFFICE WITH THE BELOW PERSPECTIVE

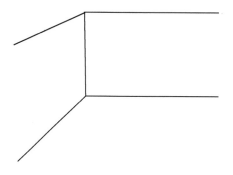

Day 67
Create a street with the below perspective

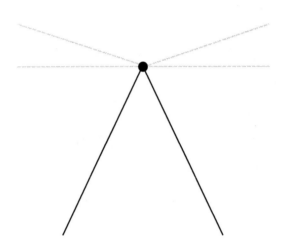

*Hint

Day 68
Draw a Vase on top of this table, make sure your vantage point matches

*Hint

The vantage point is from where one
looks at a scene. So your point of
view as the artist or audience.

DAY 69
DRAW A SCHOOL CORRIDOR USING THE BELOW PERSPECTIVE

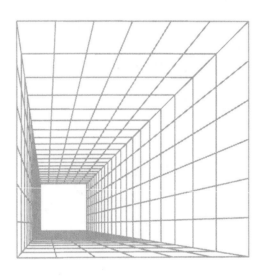

Having trouble?

Perspective can be really tough to wrap your head around. In fact, it's where most people give up with drawing.

So let's take a breather and explore some more familiar concepts for a day.

Don't give up now.

Day 70
Don't focus on getting perspective right today, instead let's get abstract!
Draw how the word 'harmony' feels

DAY 71
BUILD A CITY INSIDE THIS GLOBE, USING THE LINES TO GUIDE YOUR PERSPECTIVE

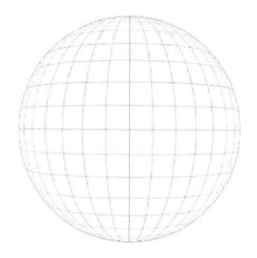

*HINT

Day 72
Draw a car with the below perspective

Day 73
Draw a railway track using the vanishing point below

*Hint

A vanishing point is a point on the
image plane of a perspective
drawing where the two-dimensional
perspective projections of mutually
parallel lines in three-dimensional
space appear to converge.

DAY 74
FINISH THIS FACE

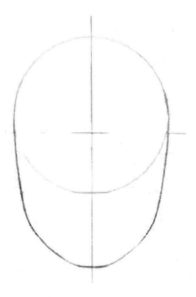

HINT

DAY 75
FINISH THE BELOW FACES FROM THREE DIFFERENT PERSPECTIVES

PHEW! 75 DAYS DOWN!

That was a tough one. Let's reflect about
perspective and how you feel it went...

My favourite drawing: _____

The most difficult prompt: _____

The most inspiring prompt:_____

I'm really good at: _____

I need to work on: _____

Build a small scene around this
glass (don't forget perspective)
ꙫ

Coming soon: 90 days!

The next 15 days will focus on still life.

Each prompt will request you to search on the internet for the image and ask you to draw exactly what you see.

This is not about realism, but rather drawing the exact proportions and emotion you see on screen. Can you scale a drawing correctly, or put to paper the image in front of you?

So let's become copy-cats and sketch what we see!

DAY 76
FIND A 'BULL' ONLINE AND DRAW WHAT YOU SEE BELOW

DAY 77
FIND A 'BROKEN MIRROR' ONLINE AND
DRAW WHAT YOU SEE BELOW

DAY 78
FIND A 'FLORAL ARRANGEMENT' ONLINE AND DRAW WHAT YOU SEE BELOW

DAY 79
FIND A 'WHALE' ONLINE AND DRAW WHAT YOU SEE BELOW

DAY 80
FIND A 'CAVE' ONLINE AND DRAW WHAT YOU SEE BELOW

DAY 81
FIND A 'FORMULA 1 RACE' ONLINE AND DRAW WHAT YOU SEE BELOW

DAY 82
FIND A 'CITY SKYLINE' ONLINE AND DRAW WHAT YOU SEE BELOW

DAY 83
FIND A 'ZOO' ONLINE AND DRAW WHAT YOU SEE BELOW

DAY 84
FIND A 'CASTLE' ONLINE AND DRAW WHAT YOU SEE BELOW

Day 85
Find a 'group of cowboys' online and draw what you see below

Day 86

Find a 'soccer ball' online and draw
what you see below

DAY 87
FIND AN 'ARCTIC EXPLORER' ONLINE AND
DRAW WHAT YOU SEE BELOW

DAY 88
FIND A '1990S TELEVISION SET' ONLINE AND DRAW WHAT YOU SEE BELOW

DAY 89
FIND A 'SPEAKEASY' ONLINE AND DRAW
WHAT YOU SEE BELOW

Day 90
Find a 'spaceship' online and draw what you see below

90 Days! Whaa?

Wow! We're almost done with our 100 Days
of Drawing! Let's reflect about the journey so
far...

My favourite drawing: _____

The most difficult prompt: _____

The most inspiring prompt:_____

I'm really good at: _____

I need to work on: _____

Finish the above cat. Can you
keep consistent with the art
style?

We're almost at 100!

What will we do with our last 10 days?!

Your final days with this sketchbook will focus on reflection, a skill that is vital to the improvement of any artist.

Each prompt will revisit a previous exercise and ask you to perhaps tackle it again, draw it in a different art style or build on the world.

So let's bring it home and finish 100 Days of Drawing!

Day 91
Revisit 'Day 1' prompt and redraw it with your new found skills!

DAY 92
REVISIT 'DAY 11' PROMPT AND REDRAW IT AS A DIFFERENT ART STYLE.

DAY 93
REVISIT 'DAY 31' PROMPT AND BUILD ON THE WORLD YOUR CHARACTER IS IN

Day 94
Revisit 'Day 34' prompt and redraw it with your new found skills!

DAY 95
REVISIT 'DAY 38' PROMPT AND REDRAW IT
AS A DIFFERENT ART STYLE.

Day 96
Revisit 'Day 41' prompt and build on the world your character is in

Day 97
Revisit 'Day 61' prompt and redraw it with your new found skills!

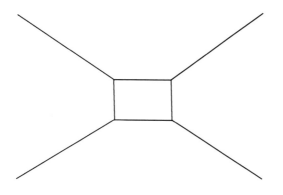

DAY 98
REVISIT 'DAY 78' PROMPT AND REDRAW IT AS A DIFFERENT ART STYLE.

DAY 99
REVISIT 'DAY 85' PROMPT AND BUILD ON THE WORLD YOUR CHARACTERS ARE IN

Day 100
Pick your least favourite drawing (or one you felt you struggled with) and re-draw it below

Congratulations!

You did it! 100 days of consistent drawing completed! That is an incredible achievement and you should feel so accomplished!

Let's reflect and rate how you feel about the process and the skills you've gained...

My creativity skills: **/10**

My world building skills: **/10**

My perspective skills: **/10**

My proportion skills: **/10**

My still life skills: **/10**

My favourite thing to draw: _____

My art style is: _____

I want to get better at: _____

Printed in Great Britain
by Amazon

35111685R00062